Grade 1
Violin

CW00408238

Chester Music
part of The Music Sales Group
London / New York / Paris / Sydney / Copenhagen / Berlin / Madrid / Hong Kong / Tokyo

6.99

Published by

Chester Music
part of The Music Sales Group
14-15 Berners Street, London W1T 3LJ, UK.

Exclusive Distributors:
Music Sales Limited
Distribution Centre, Newmarket Road,
Bury St Edmunds, Suffolk IP33 3YB, UK.

Music Sales Pty Limited
Level 4, Lisgar House,
30-32 Carrington Street,
Sydney, NSW 2000 Australia.

Order No. CH84172
ISBN 978-1-78558-074-1
This book © Copyright 2015 Chester Music Limited.
All Rights Reserved.

Unauthorised reproduction of any part of this
publication by any means including photocopying
is an infringement of copyright.

Edited by Jenni Norey.
Arranged and engraved by Christopher Hussey.
With thanks to Anna Giddey.

Printed in the EU.

Your Guarantee of Quality
As publishers, we strive to produce every book to the
highest commercial standards.
This book has been carefully designed to minimise awkward
page turns and to make playing from it a real pleasure.
Particular care has been given to specifying acid-free, neutral-sized paper
made from pulps which have not been elemental chlorine bleached.
This pulp is from farmed sustainable forests and was
produced with special regard for the environment.
Throughout, the printing and binding have been planned to
ensure a sturdy, attractive publication which should give years of enjoyment.
If your copy fails to meet our high standards,
please inform us and we will gladly replace it.

www.musicsales.com

Violin
Fingering
Chart

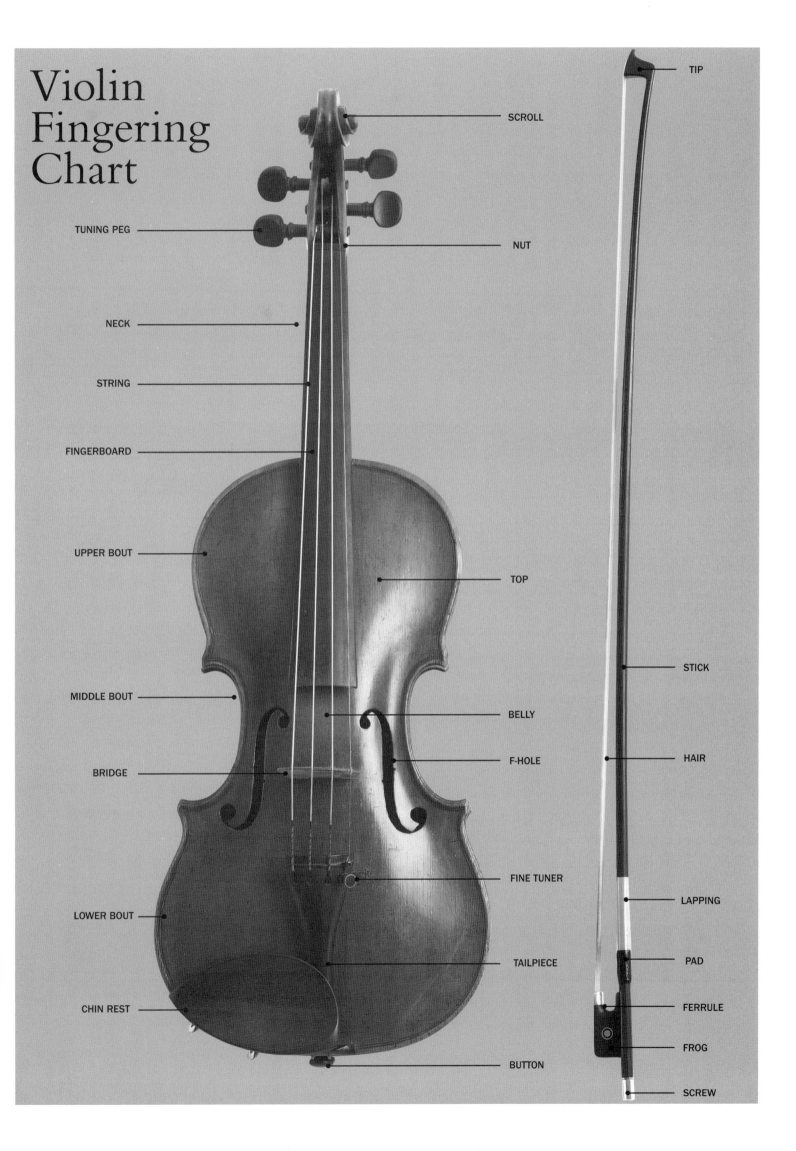

SCROLL

TUNING PEG

NUT

NECK

STRING

FINGERBOARD

UPPER BOUT

TOP

MIDDLE BOUT

BELLY

F-HOLE

BRIDGE

FINE TUNER

LOWER BOUT

TAILPIECE

CHIN REST

BUTTON

TIP

STICK

HAIR

LAPPING

PAD

FERRULE

FROG

SCREW

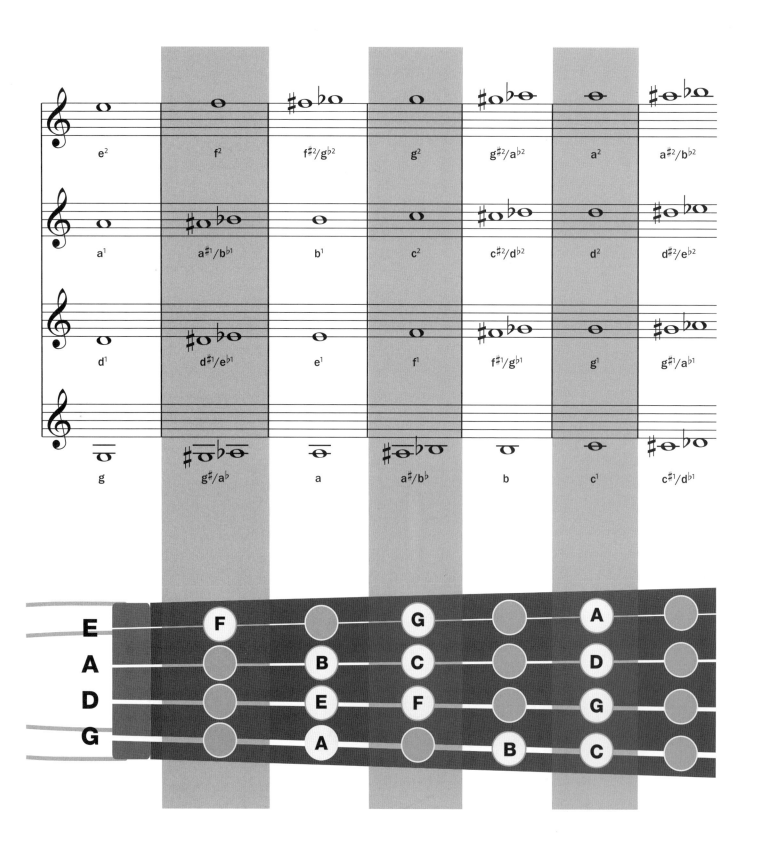

| b^2 | c^3 | $c^{\#3}/d^{\flat 3}$ | d^3 | $d^{\#3}/e^{\flat 3}$ | e^3 |

| e^2 | f^2 | $f^{\#2}/g^{\flat 2}$ | g^2 | $g^{\#2}/a^{\flat 2}$ | a^2 |

| a^1 | $a^{\#1}/b^{\flat 1}$ | b^1 | c^2 | $c^{\#2}/d^{\flat 2}$ | d^2 |

| d^1 | $d^{\#1}/e^{\flat 1}$ | e^1 | f^1 | $f^{\#1}/g^{\flat 1}$ | g^1 |

B   C   D   E

E   F   G   A

A   B   C   D

D   E   F   G

22
Taylor Swift

Released as the fourth single from her multi-platinum selling album, *Red*, '22' was written by Swift and producers Max Martin and Shellback. It remains one of her most critically acclaimed pop tracks, and the singer herself has spoken of her fondness for the song and its subject matter. In 2012 she told *Billboard* magazine: "Being 22 has been my favourite year of my life. I like all the possibilities of how you're still learning, but you know enough".

All Shook Up
Elvis

The King of Rock 'n' Roll was well into his UK chart career, having released no fewer than 10 previous hit singles, before he finally reached No. 1 with this song in July 1957, the first of 18 to top the UK charts. In the USA it was the year's No. 1 single, topping all three charts; Pop, Country and R&B, for eight weeks.

Best Song Ever
One Direction

The anthemic chorus made this song an instant pop classic, explaining why critics and Directioners alike see this as, quite possibly, the band's best song ever. The humorous video sees the lads act in quirky roles such as Harry's 'nerdy marketing guy' and Zayn's 'sexy female assistant'. Directed by actor Ben Winston and written by Winston and James Cordon, the video smashed records when it garnered 12.3 million views during its first 24 hours on Vevo.

Last Friday Night
Katy Perry

This song reached No. 1 on the *Billboard Hot 100*—the fifth song from *Teenage Dream* to reach this spot—making Perry the first female solo artist to have five No. 1 singles on the Hot 100 from the same album. The video features a few familiar faces, including Darren Criss and Kevin McHale from *Glee* plus singer-songwriter Debbie Gibson and actor Corey Feldman.

Lay All Your Love On Me
ABBA

Taken from ABBA's 1980 album *Super Trouper*, 'Lay All Your Love On Me' was released as a 12-inch single in 1981, backed with 'On And On And On'. Aimed squarely at the dance circuit, it came in at No. 60 on Slant Magazine's list of the greatest dance songs of all time.

Love Is All Around
Wet Wet Wet

First released by the The Troggs in 1967, this song really made it big when Wet Wet Wet's version was featured in the hit 1994 film *Four Weddings And A Funeral*. It quickly climbed to the No. 1 spot where it stayed for an impressive 15 weeks in a row, only to be knocked off by Whigfield's 'Saturday Night'.

Make You Feel My Love
Adele

Adele's cover of this Bob Dylan song was featured on her multi-platinum debut album *19*, which entered the UK charts at No. 1 on its release in January 2008. 'Make You Feel My Love' was the fifth and final single to be taken from the album, and though it only reached No. 26 on its initial release, it re-entered the charts after it was performed on the seventh series of *The X Factor*, eventually peaking at No. 4.

My Way
Frank Sinatra

A millionaire songwriter and performer by the age of 20, Paul Anka bought the copyright to a French song 'Comme d'Habitude' in 1966 and adapting it only slightly, came up with not only one of the greatest ballads of the 20th century, but the song most people identify as Frank Sinatra's signature tune.

Say Something
A Great Big World feat. Christina Aguilera

This sparse indie-pop ballad by American duo A Great Big World was featured on the US reality show *So You Think You Can Dance?*, where it caught the attention of Christina Aguilera, leading to a re-recording of the song featuring the singer. In an MTV News interview, co-writer Chad Vaccarino stated "We got this beautiful email from Christina saying how she didn't want to take over the song at all... she just wanted to add this texture."

A Sky Full Of Stars
Coldplay

The third single from *Ghost Stories*, co-written and produced by Swedish electronic dance music artist Avicii, this is the only dance track on the album and indeed Coldplay's first venture into the genre. On invitation from Chris Martin, Avicii also played piano on the recording.

Somethin' Stupid
Frank and Nancy Sinatra

Despite doubts about father and daughter singing a love song, Frank Sinatra gained his first gold single for the recording he made with daughter Nancy, the only example of such a combination having a No. 1 hit in the USA. In the UK, Robbie Williams' duet with actress Nicole Kidman became his first Christmas No. 1 in 2001.

Somewhere Only We Know
Lily Allen

Originally written, recorded and released by Keane in 2004, Lily Allen released her own cover of 'Somewhere Only We Know' in 2013, which was featured as the music to John Lewis' main Christmas campaign that year. The song peaked at the top of the UK singles charts, scoring Allen her third No. 1. Some of the proceeds from the sales were donated to the Save The Children disaster relief appeal in the aftermath of the Philippine typhoon.

Stay
Rihanna feat. Mikky Ekko

This song feels stripped down and intimate compared to Rihanna's more electronic, heavily produced hits. The song's lyrical themes of wanting or needing to hold onto someone are emphasised by the lack of resolution in the piano's harmonic progression. Throughout the first few choruses and verses in the song the chord progression returns time and time again to A minor, as if clinging onto the chord and feeling.

A Thousand Years
Christina Perri

Based on the best-selling series of teen vampire novels by Stephenie Meyer, *Breaking Dawn* is the last book in the *Twilight* saga, and was split into two films. Christina Perri's 'A Thousand Years' was taken from the soundtrack to part 1 of the film, though a slightly different version featuring Steve Kazee features in part 2.

Yesterday
The Beatles

One of The Beatles' most popular ballads, 'Yesterday' was written after Paul woke from a dream with the tune in his head. The song started life with the temporary title *Scrambled Eggs*; apparently, Paul and John used to substitute lyrics until they could make up suitable ones, thus this started out with the line "Scrambled eggs, oh my baby how I love your legs".

22

Words & Music by Taylor Swift, Max Martin & Johan Schuster

© Copyright 2012 Taylor Swift Music/Sony/ATV Tree Publishing/MXM Music AB, Sweden.
Sony/ATV Music Publishing/Kobalt Music Publishing Limited. All Rights Reserved. International Copyright Secured.

This piece has lots of offbeat entries where the tune starts after the first quaver beat. Keep the bow on the string during the rests so you are ready to play.

All Shook Up

Words & Music by Elvis Presley & Otis Blackwell

© Copyright 1957 Elvis Presley Music.
All Rights Reserved. International Copyright Secured.

Lean on the first of each pair of quavers to create the 'swung' effect. Remember to count the rests, and watch out for F♮ in bar 17 played with a low 1st finger.

Best Song Ever

Words & Music by Wayne Hector, John Ryan, Julian Bunetta & Edward Drewett

© Copyright 2013 BMG Platinum Songs US/Holy Cannoli Music/Music Of Big Deal/Bob Erotik Music/The Family Songbook.
Universal/MCA Music Limited/Warner/Chappell Music Publishing Limited/BMG Rights Management (US) LLC. All Rights Reserved. International Copyright Secured.

A strong pulse will give this song energy. Use the dynamics to create shape, building to the accents beginning at the end of bar 30, and then fading away to a gentle finish.

Last Friday Night

Words & Music by Max Martin, Lukasz Gottwald, Bonnie McKee & Katy Perry

© Copyright 2010 Kasz Money Publishing/When I'm Rich You'll Be My Bitch, USA/Where Da Kasz At, USA/Prescription Songs LLC, USA/Bonnie McKee Music, USA/MXM Music AB/Songs Of Pulse Recording. Kobalt Music Publishing Limited/Warner/Chappell North America Limited./BMG Rights Management (US) LLC. All Rights Reserved. International Copyright Secured.

The repeated staccato crotchets, as in bar 13, need a short, detached bow stroke. Using your 4th finger, where marked, will avoid string crossings and sound smoother.

Lay All Your Love On Me

Words & Music by Benny Andersson & Björn Ulvaeus

© Copyright 1980 Universal/Union Songs Musikforlag AB. Bocu Music Limited for Great Britain and the Republic of Ireland.
Universal Music Publishing Limited for World excluding Great Britain and the Republic of Ireland. All Rights Reserved. International Copyright Secured.

Small bows at the beginning will keep the quavers rhythmic but soft. Increase the volume from bar 25 opening out to a full, rich sound for the chorus at bar 30.

Love Is All Around

Words & Music by Reg Presley

© Copyright 1967 Dick James Music Limited. Universal/Dick James Music Limited.
All Rights Reserved. International Copyright Secured.

This love song needs gentle, smooth bowing. Remember to count carefully, especially three beats for dotted minims at the end of phrases. Don't forget to repeat back from the sign to 'Fine'.

Make You Feel My Love

Words & Music by Bob Dylan

© Copyright 1997 Special Rider Music, USA.
All Rights Reserved. International Copyright Secured.

Enjoy the ringing sound on each note of this slow song. Most of the song is quite soft, so make sure there's a contrast at bar 19 when it is marked mezzo forte (**mf**), meaning 'quite loud'.

My Way

Words by Claude Francois, Paul Anka, Jacques Revaux & Gilles Thibaut
Music by Claude Francois, Jacques Revaux & Gilles Thibaut

© Copyright 1967 Jeune Musique Editions/Barclay Eddie Nouvelles Editions. Warner/Chappell Overseas Holdings Limited/Imagem Music.
All Rights Reserved. International Copyright Secured.

Save bow on the tied minims and travel back to the heel on the up bow to avoid getting stuck at the point.
Watch out for high 3rd fingers in bars 6, 19 and 20.

Say Something

Words & Music by Mike Campbell, Chad Vaccarino & Ian Axel

© Copyright 2011 Songs Of Universal Incorporated/Chad Vaccarino Publishing/Ian Axel Music /Songtrust Blvd. Universal/MCA Music Limited/ST Music LLC.
All Rights Reserved. International Copyright Secured.

Play with a strong, solid sound on the E string in the forte (f) sections, in contrast to the soft beginning and end. Count very carefully in the bars rests.

A Sky Full Of Stars

Words & Music by Guy Berryman, Jonathan Buckland, William Champion, Christopher Martin & Tim Bergling

© Copyright 2014 Universal Music Publishing MGB Limited/EMI Music Publishing Ltd.
All Rights Reserved. International Copyright Secured.

Try counting in your head and clapping the rhythm first to get used to the tied notes. Smooth, *legato* bowing with slow bows on long notes will help this tune sing.

Somethin' Stupid

Words & Music by C. Carson Parks

© Copyright 1967 Greenwood Music Company, USA. Chester Music Limited trading as Montclare Music for the UK and Eire only.
All Rights Reserved. International Copyright Secured.

Play the quavers in the middle of the bow with a relaxed, calm feel. The phrases beginning in bars 12 and 20 grow louder and quieter again, following the shape of the tune.

Somewhere Only We Know

Words & Music by Richard Hughes, Tim Rice-Oxley & Tom Chaplin

© Copyright 2004 BMG Music Publishing Limited. Universal Music Publishing MGB Limited.
All Rights Reserved. International Copyright Secured.

Most entries are on the offbeat following a quaver rest. Notice the chorus in bar 15 starts with a crotchet on the second beat—take your time here.

Stay

Words & Music by Justin Parker & Mikky Ekko

© Copyright 2012 Sony ATV Tunes LLC/Kkids And Stray Dogs. Sony/ATV Music Publishing.
All Rights Reserved. International Copyright Secured.

The main idea in this song is repeated, but each time it is slightly different. Be careful when working out the notes and rhythms, and when counting rests.

A Thousand Years

Words & Music by David Hodges & Christina Perri

© Copyright 2011 12 06 Publishing, USA/EMI Blackwood Music Inc/Warner-Tamerlane Publishing Corp/Miss Perri Lane Publishing.
EMI Music Publishing Limited/Fintage Publishing B.V./Warner/Chappell North America Limited. All Rights Reserved. International Copyright Secured.

Keep the bowing as smooth as possible with no gaps in the sound, particularly when crossing strings as in bar 8. Notice the repeated section is loud (f) the second time.

Yesterday

Words & Music by John Lennon & Paul McCartney

© Copyright 1965 Sony/ATV Music Publishing.
All Rights Reserved. International Copyright Secured.

Look carefully at the key signature as this piece is in F major, which means low 1st fingers on the A and E strings. Watch out for the accidentals too!

123456789

COLLECT THE SERIES
Graded Violin Pieces
15 Popular Practice Pieces

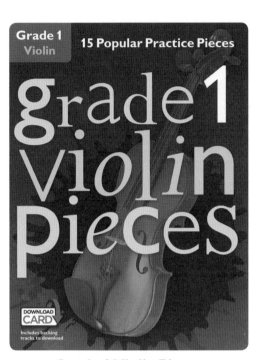

Grade 1 Violin Pieces

CH84172

Grade 2 Violin Pieces

CH84183

Grade 3 Violin Pieces

CH84194

Available from all good music shops

or, in case of difficulty contact:

Music Sales Limited, Newmarket Road, Bury St Edmunds, Suffolk, IP33 3YB, UK.

music@musicsales.co.uk

HOW TO DOWNLOAD YOUR MUSIC TRACKS

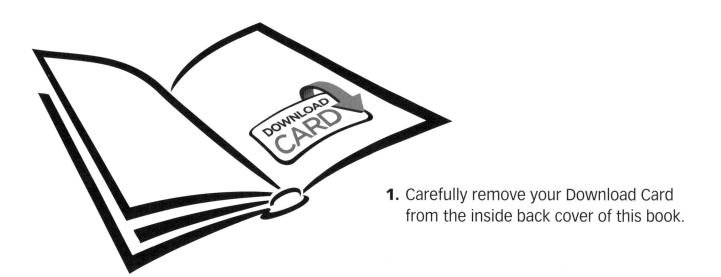

1. Carefully remove your Download Card from the inside back cover of this book.

2. On the back of the card is your unique access code. Enter this at www.musicsalesdownloads.com

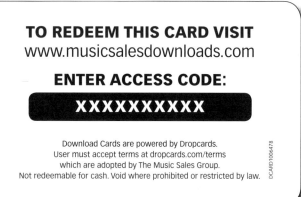

TO REDEEM THIS CARD VISIT
www.musicsalesdownloads.com

ENTER ACCESS CODE:

XXXXXXXXX

Download Cards are powered by Dropcards.
User must accept terms at dropcards.com/terms
which are adopted by The Music Sales Group.
Not redeemable for cash. Void where prohibited or restricted by law.

DCARD1006478

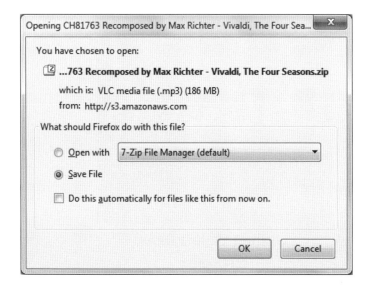

Opening CH81763 Recomposed by Max Richter - Vivaldi, The Four Sea...

You have chosen to open:

...763 Recomposed by Max Richter - Vivaldi, The Four Seasons.zip

which is: VLC media file (.mp3) (186 MB)

from: http://s3.amazonaws.com

What should Firefox do with this file?

Open with   7-Zip File Manager (default)

Save File

Do this automatically for files like this from now on.

OK   Cancel

3. Follow the instructions to save your files to your computer*. That's it!

*Appearance of download manager will vary depending upon operating system and web browser.
In case of difficulty when downloading files, please contact dropcards.com/help
Card missing? Please contact music@musicsales.co.uk